Frantic Free

167 Ways to
Calm Down & Lighten Up

PATRICIA MORGAN

LIGHT HEARTED CONCEPTS

Light Hearted Concepts
1411 – 25A Street SW
Calgary, Alberta, CANADA T3C 1J8
Web: www.solutionsforresilience.com
Email: patricia@solutionsforresilience.com
Phone: (403) 242 • 7796 / Fax: (403) 240 • 1964

Library and Archives Canada Cataloguing in Publication

Morgan, Patricia, 1946 –
   Frantic free : 167 ways to calm down and lighten up / Patricia Morgan. — 2nd ed.

Includes bibliographical references.
ISBN 978 – 0 – 9813046 – 1 – 8

   1. Stress management. I. Title.

RA785.M665 2009   155.9'042   c2009–905080–3

CREDITS:
Cover, Interior Design and Production: Jeremy Drought,
   Last Impression Publishing Service, Calgary, Alberta
Cover Art: Chandra Gilbert, Calgary, Alberta <www.chandragilbert.com>
Proofreading: Les Morgan & Edna Gilbert, Calgary, Alberta
Photo of Author: *Crystal Image Photography*, Calgary, Alberta
Printed and bound in Canada by *Friesens Corporation*, Altona, Manitoba

Contents

AT THE CITY OF CALGARY WE RECOGNIZE THAT STRENGTHENING THE WORKPLACE means helping staff be safe and well both on and off the job. We've devoted a lot of attention to the physical and social aspects of health and wellness, but we also recognize the importance of good mental health for all of our employees.

This booklet is a light-hearted basket of tips for *managing stress*, an important aspect of maintaining good mental health. It's also a token of appreciation for your valuable contribution to this organization. I hope you enjoy it.

OWEN TOBERT, PEng
City Manager

INTRODUCTION BY THE AUTHOR

HAVE YOU HAD DAYS WHEN YOU OVER-EXERCISED YOUR MIDDLE FINGER in traffic, lost your wallet, mouthed a four letter word or two and wished you hadn't got out of bed? You are not alone. In 2003 the Canadian Stress Institute reported that 45% of Canadians felt stressed out most of the time. For women, that figure rose to 52% and for married career women, 58%. But there's also good news.

Stress is our response to change. Distress happens when we do not adapt with ease, often creating dis-ease.

Surprise! We need some stress. Dr. Hans Selye called healthy stress *eustress* and too much stress *distress*. We need some challenge or stress to survive, to give meaning to our lives and a reason to get out from under the blankets. This booklet offers practical *how-to's* for managing your stress level and lightening up.

In-Joy!

Patricia

FRANTIC INVENTORY

Answer *yes* or *no* to the following questions:

	YES	NO
1. Do you believe that you are in charge of your distress levels?	○	○
2. Do you avoid perfectionist behaviours, especially during fun activities?	○	○
3. Are you comfortable in your own skin and with your own feelings?	○	○
4. Do you consciously choose positive and encouraging self talk?	○	○
5. Are you typically free of distressing discomfort such as headaches, fatigue or anxiety?	○	○
6. Are you aware of your body's distress signals?	○	○
7. Do you take time for a relationship with yourself?	○	○
8. Do you have a supportive social network?	○	○
9. Do you try to balance your needs with others' needs?	○	○
10. Do you have a healthy routine with good nutrition, rest and exercise?	○	○
11. Do you make choices in alignment with your values?	○	○
12. Have you made your home a soothing haven?	○	○
13. Do you generally say "no" when it is the best choice for you?	○	○
14. Do you keep agreements to yourself and others?	○	○

15. Are you able to laugh at yourself rather than thinking life is overwhelming? ◯ ◯

    Score: 1 point for every *yes*. **TOTAL:** ☐

Score Analysis:

BELOW 8: *Oh! Oh!* There's no time to waste. Help yourself. Highlight points in this booklet that would help you. Then act upon them.

9 – 13: *OK.* Check off the actions that would help your condition. Then act upon them.

14 – 15: *Congratulations!* Consider giving this booklet to someone who would really benefit.

NAME YOUR DISTRESS

1. List the changes that have occurred for you in the last year. Change creates stress whether it's a pleasant or painful experience. In the last year have you needed to adjust to any deaths, births, marriages, new employment, new home or health problems? The more change, the more you require rest and rejuvenation.
2. Notice your thoughts. Monitor negative and pessimistic thinking habits that create distress.

> "There is nothing good or bad, but thinking makes it so."
> **SHAKESPEARE**, *Hamlet*

3. Name and describe the energy suckers in your life — people, activities, situations and places. With whom, when and where do you feel depleted or defeated? The more you can avoid suckers, the better.
4. Identify your particular distress body symptoms — those little internal negglies that bang on your awareness and warn you of a breaking point. Pay attention before you collapse or *heart attack* yourself. There are over 100 body distress. systems. Here are some common signals: depression; anxiety or mood swings; tension headaches; fatigue; frequent colds and flu; insomnia; teeth grinding; eye twitching. For further information, go to<**http://www.stresscanada.org**>

MAKE HEALTHY LIFESTYLE CHOICES

Keep Safe

5. Wear a seat belt.
6. Drive within the speed limit.
7. Wear appropriate safety equipment.
8. If bicycling, use a helmet.
9. Spend moderate time in the sunshine.
10. Enjoy safe sex.

Participate in Medical & Dental Care

11. Have annual medical and dental check-ups.
12. Floss and brush teeth daily.

Avoid

13. Smoking.
14. Illegal drug use.
15. Consuming more than 1.5oz of liquor or 8 oz of wine a day.
16. More than three cups of caffeinated product a day.
17. Excessive amounts of the three nasty whites — white sugar, salt and flour.
18. Skipping meals, rigid diets and yo-yo dieting.

Eat and Drink

19. Drink lots of water — 6 to 8 glasses a day.
20. Include a variety of vegetables, fruits (six servings) and whole grains.
21. Eat breakfast daily.
22. Eat at least one balanced meal a day.

Rest

23. Nap for 20 minutes when needed.
24. Sleep 7 to 9 hours a day. Too many of us deprive ourselves of needed sleep to accomplish tasks but in doing so increase our errors and accidents.
25. Arrange for a massage.
26. Practice the *Relaxation Response*. Allow at least 10 minutes. Lie down. Tense each muscle group from the top of your head to your feet. Close your eyes tight for three seconds. Breathe out and let go. Now squeeze your facial muscles tight and up towards your nose for three seconds. Breathe out and let go. Continue down your body to your feet. Finally check your body from head to feet again, notice any tension, deliberately tighten and once again "let go."

"The trouble with being in the rat race is that even if you win, you're still going to be a rat."

LILY TOMLIN

27. Spend time in nature for soul soothing.

> "The average, healthy, well-adjusted adult gets up at seven-thirty
> in the morning feeling just plain terrible."
> **JEAN KERR**

Give and Take
28. Find friends who listen and share.
29. Each day tell someone, "I love you."
30. Volunteer at least twice a month.

Balance Work
31. Practice only positive gossip.
32. Take time for fun at least once a week.
33. Work overtime less than twice a month.
34. Take routine breaks.
35. Set priorities.
36. Transform "problems" to "opportunities."
37. Delegate, where possible.
38. Let the answering service serve you. Phone back when convenient.
39. Give and receive acknowledgement
    (65% of workers say they don't receive enough appreciation).
40. Recognize what you *do* accomplish.

Make Home a Comfort

41. Create fair distribution of responsibilities.
42. Hold family meetings to create cooperation. Download "Family Meetings" from "Free Articles" page at <**http://www.solutionsforresilience.com**>
43. Have discussions at mealtimes. Share the *highlights* and *lowlights* of the day.
44. Play music that either pleasingly stimulates or calms.
45. Surround yourself with enjoyable visuals — colour, furniture, pillows, artwork.
46. Add books and plants.
47. Toss some household stuff. Call to donate. Organize the rest.
48. Use bulletin boards and white boards to display and leave messages.

Manage Your Money

49. Spend less than you make.
50. Have an emergency fund (three months of living expenses) and a savings plan.

Move

51. Avoid passivity.
52. Find an exercise program or sport that works for you. Dance, walk, swim, crawl or move in some way for twenty minutes at least three times a week.
53. If you dislike exercise, ask someone to join you, perhaps a walking buddy.
54. If finances allow get a personal trainer.
55. Lift weights three times a week.
56. Love and walk a dog.

USE 30 SECOND QUICKIES

57. Breathe deeply and "swish" out stress on the out breath. Repeat.

58. Breathe in through your nose and out through your mouth. Repeat.

59. Breathe in, noticing the air coming in is cooler and the air breathed out is warmer. Be aware of cool air in and warm air out. Repeat.

60. Brush or comb your hair.

61. Chant, "Ommmm."

62. Close your eyes tight and then open.

63. Cry deeply.

64. Drum a beat.

65. File your nails.

66. Frown and then smile.

67. Growl!

68. Give and take a hug.

> *Use these anywhere, anytime. Recent research indicates that we stay healthier if regularly, even hourly, we check our body tension and release it.*

69. Hiss like a snake deeply and enthusiastically.

70. Hum a tune.

71. Kick off your shoes.

72. Lie on the floor and push your shoulder blades down.

73. Look out a window or at something beautiful like a bouquet of flowers.

74. Massage your scalp and down your cheek bones.

75. Massage your neck and shoulders.

76. Open or close a window.

77. Open or close a door.

78. Peel an orange. See, feel, smell, taste.

79. Rotate your head gently to the left and right.

80. Rub lotion on your hands and anywhere else on your body.

81. Rub your hands together.

82. Shake your right hand, then your left hand.

83. Sigh, repeat.

84. Sit down and lift your legs in the air.

85. Slowly eat a grape. Slowly eat anything.

86. Squeeze your face into a prune shape and then "let go."

87. Stand up, stretch and sit down.

88. Stick your tongue way out. Be careful who you are looking at!

89. Stomp your feet.

90. Stretch up, down, left and right.

91. Tighten your teeth and then relax.

92. Tighten all your muscles. Hold while you silently count, "1, 2, 3" and then relax.

93. Touch your toes.

94. Undo your belt.

95. Wiggle and jiggle.

96. Yawn deeply and loudly.

97. Yell and holler — especially into a pillow or in your car.

98. Zero in and enjoy a first-class belch.

FEEL YOUR FEELINGS

99. Appreciate that feelings tell you what you want, what is important, what you value and what is working for you and what is not. When you know what you want you can better take care of yourself.

100. Be aware that feelings are your internal state of being — hot, warm, cold or freezing, free, loose, centred, stretched or strained.

101. Realize that feelings tell little, if anything, about people and the world outside of ourselves. They are experienced through the body's muscles, nerves and organs. We all feel all the emotions but we each feel differently about things and experiences.

102. Discover the paradox of feelings: They (the muscular contractions, speeded breath or adrenalin flowing) calm and change as they are experienced. The feeling energy actually "lets go." Pushing away or ignoring does not work. The body can actually break down or at least experience physical pain.

103. Notice what you feel and what, if anything, you need. For example, when you are at work do you feel enlivened, neutral or perhaps burned out?

104. If your answer is *neutral*, you may ask yourself, "What can I do differently to feel *enlivened* by my work?"

105. If your answer is *burned out*, you need to ask yourself, "What do I need to do differently to look after myself?"

106. Identify your feelings and then appropriately express them. Review the sample of basic feelings in the followig matrix:

MILD	MODERATE	SEVERE
down	SAD	miserable
weary	melancholy	dejected
disappointed	HURT	crushed
taken for granted	unappreciated	deprived
uneasy	AFRAID	terrified
jittery	nervous	petrified
agitated	ANGRY	bitter
annoyed	indignant	incensed

107. Journal your feelings to discover more about yourself.
108. If feelings *haunt* you, arrange for professional support and guidance.

THINK, "SUNNY SIDE UP"

109. Read an inspiring quote, poem or book.
110. Stop telling yourself, "should've," "could've" and "would've."
111. Look at the photo of a loved one and remember a fond moment.
112. Write five resentments, then write five commitments to yourself — "From now on I will... ."
113. Write a letter expressing your frustration, then mail it or rip it up.
114. Limit and monitor television viewing. The media tends to exaggerate our culture's negative and violent side.
115. Write a NOT TO DO or I HAVE DONE list.
116. List your accomplishments in the last month.
117. Talk to a supportive listener.
118. Think, then say, "Thank you, no." Remember that *no* is the world's most powerful and effective stress reducing word.
119. If it is hard to say "no," say, "It's not good for me to say 'yes.'"
120. Give up the idea that you control anyone other than yourself.
121. View crisis as an opportunity to become creative.
122. Ask "Is there a better way for me to manage this present situation?"
123. Identify personality differences. When we accept ourselves and others as dissimilar we lessen judgment and strain. Take the personality inventory based on the MBTI at <**http://www.humanmetrics.com/cgi-win/JTypes1.htm**>

124. Reassess your values. What you focus on expands. Dedicate your energy and time to the important matters in your life. Decide what is most important to you whether it is religion, honesty, peace, compassion, nature or adventure. Act on your values.

> "You can't do what you want till you know what you're doing."
> **MOSHE FELDENKRAIS**

125. Think of five reasons to feel grateful.
126. Think of five kind acts that were done for you today.
127. Think of five things you do well.
128. Think of five reasons you love your sweetie.
129. Think of your favourite smells.
130. Think of your favourite sounds.
131. Think of your favourite people, places and activities.
132. Think of a pleasant surprise you will create for someone.
133. Think of a time in your life when you were filled with love.
134. Think of a time when someone nurtured you.
135. Think of your favourite performer.
136. Think of the most safe and relaxing moment in your life.
137. Think of yourself as perfectly imperfect.

> "The greatest weapon against stress is our ability to choose one thought over another."
> **WILLIAM JAMES**

TRANSFORM STRESSFUL THINKING

138. After identifying negative or pessimistic thoughts, deliberately create supportive and encouraging self-talk like the following examples:

Thought Distressors	**Thought De-stressors**
"Ain't it Awful?"	*"This is What Is."*

Total External:
- *It's all their fault.*   • *We are all doing the best that we can.*

Total Internal:
- *It's all my fault.*   • *I accept responsibility for my part in the problem.*

Self-victimizing:
- *They make me crazy!*   • *I have choices. I make me.*

Control Freaking:
- *They should behave!*   • *I can trust others to live life their way.*

Emotions Rule:
- *I feel stupid so it must be true.*
- *Feelings are merely body experiences carrying a personal message.*

Glum Guilt:
- *I blew it. I made a mistake.*
- *Mistakes are opportunities to learn.*

Futile Futurizing: **(worrying)**
- *What if ...?*
- *I will do the best I can with the information I have.*

Boxed in Boredom:
- *I give up. Life is meaningless.*
- *I create my own meaning.*

Petty Perfection:
- *I have to do it perfectly.*
- *It is OK to do "good enough," especially when fun is involved.*

Second Class Self-Esteem:
- *I don't matter.*
- *I am lovable.*

"Ninety-nine percent of things you worry about don't happen;
the other one percent you can't do anything about, so why worry at all?"
LOIS HOLE

SAY NO, YES OR IT DEPENDS

139. After you receive a request, pause and ask yourself, "What is the consequence to me and others if I say *no*, *yes* or *it depends*?"
140. Give yourself time to consider the request; "I'd like to think about it."
141. Repeat the request before saying, "Thank you for asking but *no*."
142. Offer an alternative; "*No*, but what I will do is..."
143. Suggest someone else who is better suited to do the task.
144. When appropriate, explain why you are saying no; "I say *no* because..."
145. State the conditions you require to meet a request; "I will after I finish this assignment."
146. For those who find it hard to hear *no* emphatically say, "I'm giving you a *no*."
147. Give an alternative and good use of your talent when turning down a request; "The most effective use of my time is..."
148. Show you care; "I hear you are in a bind and I wish I could do more but..."

FOLLOW 7 STEPS TO CALM

149. Name your distress.
150. "Watch" a breath go in your nostrils, into your heart, through your lungs and fill your belly.
151. "Watch" that same breath go out and imagine it flowing out your toes.
152. Think of a pleasurable moment, perhaps from a distant time.
153. Ask "Is there a better way for me to manage this present situation?"
154. Use your mind to follow the direction of your heart.
155. Take action or accept the present situation *as is*.

"God grant me the SERENITY to accept the things I cannot change;
COURAGE to change the things I can; and WISDOM to know the difference."
REINHOLD NIEBUHR

USE LIGHT HEARTED STRATEGIES

156. Smile.

157. Laugh especially when you don't know what to do.

158. Goof Off. Take some time and "waste" it well.

159. Play the Bad News/Good News Game. For example: The Bad News is my boss told me, "Your calculations are off. Redo the report. The Good News is, "This gives me a chance to redo the calculations and build in a pay hike just for me." Just kidding!

160. Exaggerate your woes. Ask a friend or support person to listen, without offering solutions. Wallow, wail, whine, groan and cry. Maybe the two of you will end up laughing.

161. Treat yourself. On particularly distressful days give yourself an extra dose of pampering: a nap, chocolate, a bubble bath, a pedicure, movie, popcorn.

"There must be quite a few things a hot bath won't cure, but I don't know many of them."
SYLVIA PLATH

162. Buy and play with some fun props like chattering teeth or windup toys.

163. Tell a *clean* joke.

164. Memorize fun and cheerful songs. Sing to yourself or out loud. One of my favourites is "You Are My Sunshine."

165. Write silly ditties. For example, transform *Mary Had a Little Lamb*,

> *Suzy had a stressful day.*
> *Mistakes where e'er she'd go.*
> *And no matter where she parked*
> *The meter man would know.*

166. Use playful and affirming self-talk:

- *"It could be worse. I could be dead."*
- *"What other people think of me is none of my business."*
- *"There's always somebody doing better and somebody doing worse than me. At least I have me."*
- *"A weakness named can become a strength."*
- *"Just like the Little Red Engine, 'I think I can. I know I can.'"*
- *"Maybe the biggest joke of my life is my seriousness. It must be an illusion of grandeur to imagine I am so important."*

167. If you find this list too long, focus on the following 8 Stress Reduction Essentials and let the rest go.

8 STRESS REDUCTION ESSENTIALS

1. Have a daily body/mind supportive routine.
2. Observe your body/emotional signals and attend to them.
3. Witness your stress-creating thoughts (or beliefs). Challenge and change them.
4. Say "no" to unsatisfying activities or organizations demanding your time.
5. Avoid workaholism at home, work or in your community.
6. Eat consciously with more vegetables and less sugar, salt and flour.
7. Exercise to create a strong body and to give your mind a rest.
8. Consider that the biggest distress may be your seriousness. Lighten up!

> "In the end, it's not going to matter how many breaths you took,
> but how many moments took your breath away."
>
> **SHING XIONG**

ADDITIONAL RESOURCES

Stress Focused

Axelrod, A. & Holtje, J. (1997). *201 ways to say no gracefully and effectively.* Columbus, OH: McGraw-Hill.

Braham, B.J. (1991). *Calm down: How to manage stress at work.* Toronto, ON: Harper Collins, Canada

Carson, R. (2003). *Taming your gremlin: A surprisingly simple method for getting out of your own way.* SanFrancisco, CA: HarperSanFrancisco.

Markham, U. (2002). *The ultimate stress handbook for women.* London, UK: Collins & Brown.

Roizen, M.(1999). *Real age: Are you as young as you can be?* New York, NY: Cliff Street Books.

Roizen, M., Oz, M., Oz, L., & Spiker, T. (2005). *You: The owner's manual: An insider's guide to the body that will make you healthier and younger.* New York, NY: HarperCollins.

Rosenberg, M. (2003). *Nonviolent communication: A language of life.* Encinitas, CA: Puddle Dancer Press.

Selye, H.(1974). *Stress without distress.* Toronto, ON: Signet Books.

Siebert, A. (2005). *The resiliency advantage: Master change, thrive under pressure, and bounce back from setbacks.* San Francisco, CA: Berrett-Koehler.

———. (1996). *The survivor personality.* New York, NY: Perigee Books.

Light Hearted Perspectives

Barreca, R. (1991). They used to call me Snow White but I drifted: Women's strategic use of humor. Adams, MA: Viking.

Cousins, N. (2005). Anatomy of an illness as perceived by the patient. New York, NY: W.W. Norton & Co.

Kerr, M. (2001). You can't be serious! Putting humor to work. Canmore, AB: Humor at Work Institute.

LaRoche, L. (1998) Relax—you may only have a few minutes left. New York, NY: Random House.

Seligman, M. (2004). Authentic happiness: Using the new positive psychology to realize your potential for lasting fulfillment. New York, NY: Free Press, Simon & Schuster.

Wooten, P. (2002). Compassionate laughter: Jest for your health. Santa Cruz, CA: Jest Press.

Websites:

For stress symptom inventory: <**http://www.stresscanada.org/**>

For big time stress: <**http://www.teachhealth.com/**>

For healthy lifestyle: <**www.realage.com/index.aspx**>

For enhancing and calming your primary relationship:
<**www.banffcouplesconference.com**>

For resiliency strengthening: <**http://www.resiliencycenter.com/**> and
<**www.solutionsforresilience.com**>

For integrating humor: <**www.jesthealth.com**>

BOOKS BY PATRICIA MORGAN

FROM WOE TO WOW: HOW RESILIENT WOMEN SUCCEED AT WORK

From Woe to WOW provides solutions and easy-to-implement actions
for dealing with workplace challenges and life's adversities.

"From Woe to WOW is a wonderful, practical, inspirational tool for women and all those who support them."
DR. ROBERT NEAULT, Author of *Career Strategies for Lifetime Success*

LOVE HER AS SHE IS: LESSONS FROM A DAUGHTER STOLEN BY ADDICTIONS
A True Story with 14 Ways to Demonstrate Unconditional Love

"Patricia Morgan and her daughter Kelly have written a book that is searingly honest. ...most
important of all, there are solutions in this book—tools and techniques to move us all forward.
This mother and daughter have been through hell. What they have to say can put out some
of those hell-fires for *you*."
DR. SIDNEY B. SIMON
Professor Emeritus, University of Massachusetts. Author of *Values Clarification* and other books

SHE SAID: A TAPESTRY OF WOMEN'S QUOTES

She Said: A Tapestry of Women's Quotes is a thoughtful gift especially for women to
express appreciation or affection. She Said is filled with wise and witty words by women
from the world over.

"This is a fabulous tribute to women!"
FRANCES WRIGHT, Founder, Famous 5 Foundation

Two Ways to Enrich your Next Meeting or Conference

1. Invite Patricia Morgan to Speak to Your Group

Patricia Morgan is an author and expert in strengthening resilience in individuals and organizations. With a Master's Degree in Psychology she offers practical how-to's that decrease self-doubt, stress and miscommunication while increasing vitality, productivity and workplace satisfaction. Plus she delivers her message in a fun, insightful and uplifting manner. She confidently affirms, "You're stronger than you think."

2. Order a Copy of this Booklet for Everyone in Your Organization

Quantity discounts make this booklet a valuable resource for your next event by creating a memorable impact. Send your people away with do-able ways to better manage their distress and increase their resilience.

To book Patricia Morgan for your next event and/or to order *Frantic Free* in quantity, call **(403) 242·7796** or visit Patricia's website at <**www.solutionsforresilience.com**>

PLEASE NOTE: this publication can be customized and imprinted with your organization's logo and an introductory note from your leadership.

ENDORSEMENTS OF PATRICIA MORGAN

"Just being in the same room as Patricia Morgan is a stress reliever."

KAY OLSEN, *Women in Business*
Medicine Hat, AB

"We laughed. We learned. We walked away with useful tools to better take care of ourselves. Patricia pressure proofed the women of Ipswich."

JONI BIRCH, *Relationships Australia*
Brisbane, Queensland

"Patricia is a breath of fresh air. Her genuine and customized approach to presenting is truly spectacular. We were so pleased with her keynote for our annual conference, we asked her to present again four years later and she is more dynamic than ever."

SHEILA MCCONNELL, *Addictions Ontario*
Mississauga, ON